The Old Fashioned Rules of Grammar Book

The no-nonsense, proudly old-fashioned rules of grammar to learn and remember for life

 Ward Lock Educational Co. Ltd.

WARD LOCK EDUCATIONAL CO. LTD.
1 CHRISTOPHER ROAD
EAST GRINSTEAD
SUSSEX RH19 3BT

A MEMBER OF THE LING KEE GROUP
HONG KONG · SINGAPORE · LONDON · NEW YORK

First published – 1979
Reprinted – 1980,1981,1992

ISBN 0-7062-3850-8

Note to the reader

Pencil in your answers lightly so that you can rub
them out and practise again. You can check your
answers at the back of the book.

Other titles in this series:

The Old Fashioned Rules of Punctutation Book
ISBN 0 7062 4123 1

The Old Fashioned Rules of Spelling Book
ISBN 0 7062 4085 5

The Old Fashioned Handwriting Book
ISBN 0 7062 4139 8

The Old Fashioned Multiplication Book
ISBN 0 7062 4121 5

The Old Fashioned Division Book
ISBN 0 7062 4122 3

The Old Fashioned Adding-Up Book
ISBN 0 7062 4086 3

The Old Fashioned Taking-Away Book
ISBN 0 7062 4148 7

The Old Fashioned Mental Arithmetic Book
ISBN 0 7062 4160 6

The Old Fashioned Times Table Book
ISBN 0 7062 3749 8

Printed in Hong Kong

The Old Fashioned Rules of Grammar

A Noun's the name of any thing
As *school,* **or** *garden, hoop* **or** *swing.*

Adjectives describe the kind of noun
As *great, small, pretty, white* **or** *brown.*

Instead of nouns the Pronouns fit —
As *he, you, they* **and** *it.*

Verbs tell of something being done —
To *read, write, count, sing, jump* **or** *run.*

How, when and where the Adverbs tell,
As *slowly, near, now* **or** *well.*

Conjunctions join the words together,
As men *and* **women, wind** *or* **weather.**

The preposition stands before
A Noun, as *in* **or** *through* **a door.**

The interjection shows surprise,
As *Oh,* **how pretty,** *Ah,* **how wise.**

Three little words you often see,
Are Articles *a, an* **and** *the.*

The whole are called Nine Parts of Speech,
Which reading, writing, speaking teach.

Nouns

A Noun's the name of any thing
As *school* **or** *garden, hoop* **or** *swing.*

Here are some more nouns:

boat, house, shoe, toy

Write one noun for each letter of
the alphabet.
The first one is done for you.

a apple . . . .   n . . . .

b . . . .   o . . . .

c . . . .   p . . . .

d . . . .   q . . . .

e . . . .   r . . . .

f . . . .   s . . . .

g . . . .   t . . . .

h . . . .   u . . . .

i . . . .   v . . . .

j . . . .   w . . . .

k . . . .   x . . . .

l . . . .   y . . . .

m . . . .   z . . . .

Adjectives

Adjectives describe the kind of noun
As *great, small, pretty, white* **or** *brown.*

Write an adjective to go with each
of these nouns. The first one is done for you.

beautiful . . . . **princess**

. . . . **grass**

. . . . **spider**

. . . . **dog**

. . . . **river**

. . . . **witch**

. . . . **lemonade**

. . . . **worm**

. . . . **fire**

. . . . **tree**

. . . . **giant**

. . . . **town**

. . . . **door**

. . . . **soldier**

Pronouns

Instead of nouns the Pronouns fit —
As *he, you, they* **and** *it.*

Here are some more pronouns:

she, him, we, them, I, me
us, ours, yours, mine, theirs

Write a sentence using one or more
of these pronouns.
The first one is done for you.

They could not find it.

....

....

....

....

....

....

....

....

....

....

Verbs

Verbs tell of something being done —
To *read, write, count, swing, jump* **or** *run.*

How many verbs can you find beginning
with these letters. Some of the lines
have been started for you.

a attack ....

b ....

d ....

f ....

h help ....

j jump ....

l ....

m ....

p ....

r run ....

t ....

w ....

Adverbs

**How, when and where the Adverbs tell,
As** *slowly, here, now* **or** *well.*

Here are some more adverbs:

**quickly, fiercely, clearly, soon
here, yesterday, tomorrow, everywhere**

**Write a sentence using each of these adverbs.
The first one is done for you.**

I am going to the cinema tomorrow.

....

....

....

....

....

....

....

....

....

....

Conjunctions

Conjunctions join the words together,
As men *and* women, wind *or* weather.

Here are some more conjunctions:

if, because, while
but, when, although

Write a sentence using each of these
conjunctions. The first one is done for you.

I can go out if it stops raining.

....

....

....

....

....

....

....

....

....

....

Prepositions

The Preposition stands before a noun as *in, from* or *through* the town.

Here are some more prepositions:

on, by, between
under, for, at, with, to

Write a sentence using each of these prepositions. The first is done for you.

The man hid under the bridge.

. . . .

. . . .

. . . .

. . . .

. . . .

. . . .

. . . .

. . . .

. . . .

. . . .

Interjections

The Interjection shows surprise,
As *Oh,* **how pretty,** *Ah,* **how wise.**

Eh, Ugh, Hey, Oh, Ah

Put an interjection at the beginning of each sentence:

"................, speak up, I can't hear you."

"................, I don't like this food."

"................, don't leave me behind."

"................, what a beautiful sight."

"................, it is good to see you again."

Write some more sentences using interjections.

. . . .

. . . .

. . . .

. . . .

. . . .

. . . .

. . . .

The Articles — a, an and the

Three little words you often see,
Are Articles *a, an* and *the*.

Complete these sentences using *the:*

I caught . . . . . . last bus home.

I picked . . . . . . largest apple on the tree.

Here is . . . . . . Lord Mayor of London.

I am going to . . . . . north of England.

Complete these sentences using *a* or *an:*

I travel to work on . . . . . . train.

My friend is staying in . . . . . . hotel.

It took him . . . . . . hour to do the work.

He sat on . . . . . . chair.

**The whole are called Nine Parts of Speech,
Which reading, writing, speaking teach.**

**Write three examples for each of the
following:**

Noun ....

Adjective.....................................

Pronoun ....

Verb ....

Adverb..

Conjunction ....

Preposition ....

Interjection ....